TRINITY
COLLEGE LONDON

CW00677299

Piano
Grade 2

Pieces & Exercises
for Trinity College London examinations

2012-2014

Published by
Trinity College London

Registered Office:
89 Albert Embankment
London SE1 7TP UK

T +44 (0)20 7820 6100
F +44 (0)20 7820 6161
E music@trinitycollege.co.uk
www.trinitycollege.co.uk

Registered in the UK
Company no. 02683033
Charity no. 1014792

Printed in England by Halstan & Co. Ltd, Amersham, Bucks.

Menuet

from *Suite quatrième pour le clavecin*

Johann Mattheson
(1681-1764)

Dynamics and articulation are editorial.
The repeats should be played in the examination.

Bourrée in D minor

Anonymous

3

Scherzo

from *Divertimento in F*, Hob XVI/9

Franz Joseph Haydn
(1732-1809)

Dynamics and slurs are editorial.

Andante

Daniel Steibelt
(1765-1823)

Dynamics and slurs are editorial.

5

Mazurka

from *Album for the Young* op. 39

Pyotr Ilyich Tchaikovsky
(1840-1893)

Gaik (Mayday Dance)

from *Melodie Ludowe*

Witold Lutosławski
(1913–1994)

Petit Mystère

Simone Plé
(1897-1986)

Composer's metronome mark ♩ = 60.

Summer Swing

John DeHolt

Fanfare for the Common Cold

Herbert Chappell

(1) Two octaves higher (✗ = approximate pitch).

(2) The words 'Aaah! ... choo!!!' need not be spoken in the examination.

(3) Exact pitches not required – right fist/forearm cluster on black notes and left fist/forearm cluster on white notes.

Exercises

1a. Weird Waltz – tone, balance and voicing

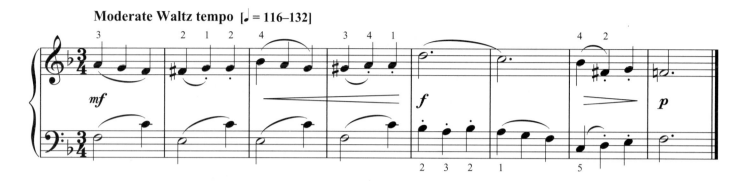

1b. The Manatee Parade – tone, balance and voicing

2a. Contrasts in Touch – co-ordination

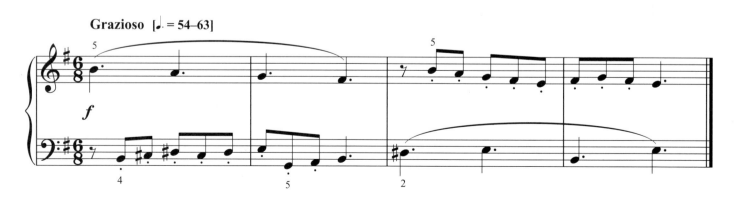

14

2b. Rag Doll – co-ordination

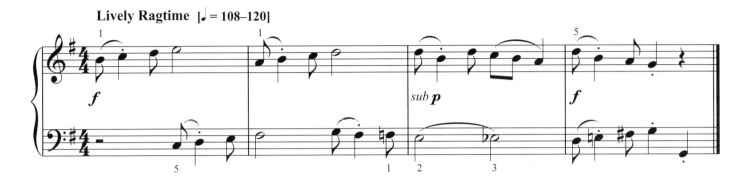

3a. Leading with the Right – finger & wrist strength and flexibility

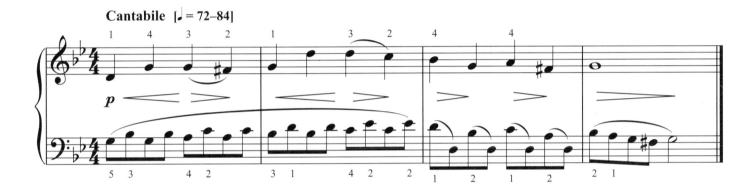

3b. Chinese Dragons – finger & wrist strength and flexibility

Pieces – Three pieces to be performed

Piece 1:	Piece 2:	Piece 3:
Chosen from this book *or* from those in the alternatives list	Chosen from this book *or* from those in the alternatives list	Chosen from this book *or* from those in the alternatives list *or* candidate's own composition (see current syllabus for details)

Technical Work – All sections and options to be prepared

i) Scales – the examiner will request a selection in the examination

Bb and D major				
G and B minor (candidate's choice of *either* harmonic *or* melodic minor)	f *or* p	legato	two octaves	hands together
Chromatic scale in similar motion starting on Bb				

ii) Arpeggios – the examiner will request a selection in the examination

Bb and D major	mf	legato	two octaves	hands separately
G and B minor				

iii) Exercises – candidates to prepare 1a *or* 1b; 2a *or* 2b; and 3a *or* 3b (three exercises in all)

1a. Weird Waltz	*or* 1b. The Manatee Parade	for tone, balance and voicing
2a. Contrasts in Touch	*or* 2b. Rag Doll	for co-ordination
3a. Leading with the Right	*or* 3b. Chinese Dragons	for finger & wrist strength and flexibility

Supporting Tests – Two tests are to be chosen from:

Sight Reading	Aural	Improvisation	Musical Knowledge

Please refer to the current syllabus for details on all elements of the examination.

Piano Pieces & Exercises for Trinity College London examinations 2012-2014

Expertly chosen, graded and edited repertoire pieces and exercises for the Trinity College London Piano Grade 2 examination.

This new selection of nine pieces encompasses a wide range of styles and genres. The exercises have been newly composed for this syllabus.

Not only selected with Trinity examinations in mind, this series provides progressive steps in performance for all piano students.

A CD of all the repertoire pieces for the grade – both those in this book and also all the alternative pieces on the syllabus – is also available. Performed by Pamela Lidiard.

To assist with preparation for this Grade examination, the following Trinity publications are also available from your local music shop:

Piano Examination Pieces Grade 2 2012-2014 CD	TG 009753	ISBN 978-0-85736-211-7
Piano Scales & Arpeggios Initial-Grade 5	TG 006103	ISBN 978-0-85736-038-0
Sound at Sight Piano book 1 (Initial-Grade 2)	TG 009180	ISBN 978-0-85736-166-0
Piano Teaching Notes 2012-2014	TG 009227	ISBN 978-0-85736-170-7

Aural Tests book 1 (Initial-Grade 5)	TG 005939	ISBN 978-0-85736-008-3
Theory Workbook Grade 2	TG 006516	ISBN 978-0-85736-001-4
A4 Manuscript book	TG 009388	ISBN 978-0-85736-186-8
Student Practice Notebook	TG 008763	ISBN 978-0-85736-017-5

   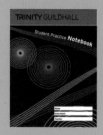

All syllabuses and further information about
Trinity College London can be obtained from:

Trinity College London
89 Albert Embankment
London SE1 7TP UK

T +44 (0)20 7820 6100
F +44 (0)20 7820 6161
E music@trinitycollege.co.uk
www.trinitycollege.co.uk/music

TG 009029
ISBN 978-0-85736-150-9

9 780857 361509

John O'Neill

PLUS CD

The JAZZ Method *for* **CLARINET**

SCHOTT
EDUCATIONAL
PUBLICATIONS

ED 12440